Pursuing Private Practice:
10 Steps To Start Your Own Business

Jennifer McGurk, RDN, CDN, CEDRD-S

Parker Press Publishing

Nyack, NY

Published by Parker Press Publishing
99 Main Street, Suite 204
Nyack NY 10960

www.pursuingprivatepractice.com
Any inquires please contact 845-535-9092

Editor: Affordable Editing Services

Cover Design: Simply Cre8tive Design Studio

ISBN 978-0-9971083-2-3

Printed in the United States of America

10 9 8 7 6 5 4 3 2

This is the Start to An Incredible Journey...

To my fellow healthcare professionals,

Congratulations on wanting to start a private practice and for deciding to use this book as your guide. Maybe you're just looking into the idea about starting a business and don't know how to start. Maybe you've decided to leave your safe 9-to-5 job to start your own practice within the next year. Or maybe you quit yesterday, and are now freaking out because you realize you lost your steady paycheck. Don't worry, this book is for every one of you!

It was an honor to write this book for you, and I'm pleased that you chose me as your guide. If you have the passion and drive, I've outlined the steps to take so you can achieve your goals. Starting a private practice can be overwhelming, but this guide will show you how it's done, with easy-to-follow steps. While you might get impatient at times, keep the end results in mind: working your own hours, having an overflow of clients, and gaining increased financial success. It takes time to build a practice, and sometimes you need to take it one step at a time. This book will help you along the way, showing you exactly how to achieve your business goals. The end is worth it—your own successful business with YOU as your own boss.

This book is all about starting your own business. We'll talk about setting up a private practice that works for you and your personality. We go into finding your business passion and setting up your business plan, followed by legally forming your business and getting your finances, insurance, and counseling space set up. We'll also talk about getting medical records, assessment forms, and handouts together. We'll end with what to charge your clients, or at least how to start thinking about the financial part of owning a business.

Along the way you'll see some of my personal tips with the intro "By the way...". You'll also find advice from other professionals in various fields. All of this advice can be taken or ignored depending on your type of practice and your personal needs. Some hyperlinks are included in this book to lead you to various websites for more information. Please visit www.pursuingprivatepractice.com/hyperlinks to find those links in one place for you. There are also some affiliate links included, which means if you visit the site and purchase a product, I receive a small profit. These affiliate links are clearly marked with (affiliate link).

I look forward to hearing about your successful practice!

Sincerely,

Jennifer McGurk, RDN, CDN, CEDRD-S

Table of Contents

Step One: Decide to Be an Entrepreneur

Are You an Entrepreneur?

You must be! It's the entrepreneurial spirit in you that made you pick up this book. With the drive to succeed and the right resources, you can own your own successful business. An entrepreneur is "a person who organizes, manages, and assumes the risks of a business or enterprise". Entrepreneurs are hard-working individuals who are passionate about their business and want to work for themselves. Certain personality traits or characteristics are common to entrepreneurs, such as risk-taking, flexibility, and the drive to succeed.

Do you imagine yourself in certain situations where you want to lead? Do you think of yourself as a boss? Do you want to take the risk in having full control of your own career? Are you ready for a better work/life balance? If you said "yes" to any of these questions, you've got the makings of an entrepreneur.

Is Private Practice For You?

A private practice is "a business in which an individual engages in his or her profession as an independent provider, rather than as an employee". A private practice in the healthcare field could be a large company or a sole provider, with work ranging from counseling to consulting.

Many professions in the healthcare field are perfect for going into private practice, such as dietitians, psychologists, social workers, psychiatrists, doctors, and fitness professionals. We're known as people who want to help others, and we probably got into these professions to make an impact on other's mental and/or physical lives. Many professionals feel frustrated in traditional jobs—for many reasons. Usually a boss or another person is "in charge" of the work they do, and may dictate how to practice the profession. They're also expected to see a certain number of people in a short time. How much of an impact can someone really make in a 10-minute nutrition education session? How can a therapist have the energy to see 10 difficult clients in one day? Imagine a world where you get to actually have a positive impact on a client's health by taking the time to establish a good working relationship, build trust, AND get paid well for it.

By the way...

I started my private practice for many reasons. I have a leadership personality, and wanted to be in charge of my career. I also wanted a flexible schedule, and I wanted to make more money for my time! These reasons were all important to me, but the number one reason I started my private practice was so that I could become my own boss.

The Multiple Benefits of Owning a Practice

Starting your own private practice is a very scary decision, but when your practice is successful, the payoffs are lucrative in career growth, money, time, and most importantly, satisfaction! Professionals in private practice have the ability to charge what they're worth and not settle for a salary. The following are just a few of the positives about private practice:

You Feel Rewarded for Hard Work

When a professional decides to go into private practice, hard work really does pay off. The rewards of client relationships make you feel like you're truly making a difference in someone's life and well-being. Clients will value your opinion and advice, giving you the level of respect you deserve as a healthcare professional. You also feel financial reward because entrepreneurs have the ability to make more money than an employee.

You Find Passion in Your Work

Your own practice is a reflection of your style and personality. What kind of work do you love to do? As a healthcare professional, you're trained to do a variety of things. But what would you do all day—if you could? What do you get excited about? What do you read about on your own, versus having to read for work? As a therapist, what training excites you? Do you want to see individuals or families or both? As a dietitian, do you want to work with mindful eating or meal plans? Or are you a doctor who wants to focus on just one specialty? Just remember, you are in full control of who you see and what you specialize in when you have a private practice.

By the way...

I love working with clients who have eating disorders, because it's a topic I'm very passionate about. I also like working with clients for long periods of time, seeing them discover the power of a healthy relationship with food. Getting to know my clients is very personal, and something I could never do in a hospital or clinic setting, where a boss told me how much time I have with someone.

You Create Your Own Schedule

Private practice counselors have the benefit of creating their own work hours. Are you a morning person who wants to work early? Or are you a night owl who wants to work later in the afternoon and evening? Or are you a mom, and can only work while your children are in daycare or school? Having your own practice lets you decide when you see clients; you have full control over your own schedule and how much you want to work. You can take on as few or as many people as you want. You could also do consulting work as part of your practice, and therefore, there are opportunities to work more if you need or want to. You can even work less if life gets in the way, or you're making sufficient income to allow you more freedom to use your time as you see fit.

You Grow at Your Own Pace

In private practice, most counselors start small, and expand according to how much work they can or are willing to put into their business. Remember, there's no right way to grow! Some people quit their "day job" and jump in all at once, while others have a full-time job and do private practice on the side for a few hours every week. It's important to remember that a business takes time to grow and that success usually does not happen overnight. It's a journey of figuring out what works for you and your life, as well as for your business.

Most dietitians and therapists do have a part-time or full-time job when they start a business. It's especially helpful to have the flexibility in your job, if possible, so you can devote adequate time to your business, as necessary. Always remember to try to distinguish your practice from your job. Both need your attention and time, and one is not more important than the other.

By the way...

When I first started my business, I had to work hard at letting go of my "all or nothing" attitude. I used to think "Well, if I can't do it full-time, I shouldn't do it at all." Once I got over that, I started my business when I had two part-time jobs that paid my bills. I started off with just one day per week in private practice and grew from there. Eventually, I left one of my part-time jobs, and soon after, left the other one. I didn't let the "all-or-nothing" attitude stop me from taking it one step at a time and growing at a comfortable pace that worked for me.

A lot of the time, while still working for an employer, you want to take what you've learned in the job setting and apply it to your part-time private practice. If you're using the same skill sets in "work" and "private practice", can you differentiate between the two? Can you set up a practice location in a different area of town? Can you see private practice clients on weekends instead of during the traditional workweek? Don't let a regular job stop your practice, but you don't want your practice to conflict with your regular job. You'll end up being frustrated with both.

On the other hand, sometimes you want to go into a completely different area in private practice—and that's okay too. Maybe your regular job has you working with adults, but you'd rather see children in your private practice. Or maybe, you work in a healthcare setting with one particular job emphasis, but want to focus on a different area in your private practice. These two different jobs wouldn't interfere with one another. You just need to be sure you have the skills and expertise for both.

By the way...

As I was starting my private practice, I was also doing outpatient nutrition counseling jobs at the same time. But these jobs were always at least 45 minutes away from my private practice location, thus allowing me to keep them separate. I also worked at a college, where my services were exclusive to students at that school, again keeping "work" separate from my practice. At times, I would see outpatient jobs advertised that were closer to my home. I was always interested, but I knew it might hurt my business, and that was my ultimate career goal.

You Are Your Own Boss

Perhaps this is the best part! When you have your own practice, you're in control of what you do—because YOU are the boss. You call the shots and make the decisions. You're in control of the direction of your career and the outcome. You ultimately get to decide what to do with your time each day. If you're driven, you can climb all the way to the top, because there's nothing stopping you.

The Sky is the Limit

When you have your own practice, there's no upper limit to what you can do with your career. That's the benefit of being in control! Private practice can lead you to incredible networking opportunities—connections you never thought you would make, and an amazing work/life balance that you get to choose.

Step Two: Find Passion in Your Work and Pick Your Niche

Close your eyes and imagine your ideal professional job. What are you doing? What area of expertise are you working in? Are you just working with clients, or are you speaking, writing, or doing other consulting projects? Where are you located? Are you in an office building or doing home visits? Are you a sole practitioner or working with other colleagues? What are your professional strengths that you offer to clients? These are all important questions to answer as you think about your niche for your business.

When You Love It, It's Not Work

Most healthcare professionals want to feel good about the work they do. We have a drive for helping people, but we also want to feel appreciated for all that we do. Let's face it—everyone wants to feel like "work" isn't work. Having passion is defined as an intense emotion and compelling enthusiasm. This isn't traditional work! When it comes to passion, think about what topics you're most interested in, and which ones are easy for you to talk about. What skills would you like to practice, and what type of clients do you want to work with?

When you love what you do, working on business issues won't seem like a job. Your passion will ignite a powerful force inside of you to help you create the career that you want. Success in private practice requires a business owner to work hard. However, private practice "work" is driven by enthusiasm for your business, so it may not seem "hard" at all.

By the way…

I've never been happier at "work" since owning my own business. My sense of accomplishment is strong, and I love being in control of my career. I was honestly always a "good employee", but I'm much more satisfied working for myself and channeling that enthusiasm into the work that I do with clients. I truly enjoy helping eating disorder clients, and I really wouldn't want to see other types of clients—because I honestly don't love other issues as much.

Jill Lewis, MA, LCSW, CEDS, PC is the owner of <u>Jill Lewis Therapy</u>. She is a Licensed Clinical Social Worker and a Certified Eating Disorders Specialist in New York City. She provides therapy for individuals, groups, couples, and families, and for people struggling with anorexia, bulimia, and compulsive overeating.

To Specialize or Not to Specialize?

It's impossible to be an expert in many different areas. As a healthcare professional, you were trained adequately in the basics of your profession, and may have the ability to see various types of clients with various types of issues. Just because someone is capable of seeing "everyone", doesn't mean that he or she should.

It's important to note that some people love doing everything, and consider themselves a general specialist. A perfect example of this is a primary care physician. It's important to say that you are a generalist and not a specialist in 20 different areas. You'll just look foolish, because everyone knows you can't be an expert in everything. Specializing means focusing on one particular issue.

It's important to pick a few specialties that you love. By selecting a few focus areas that you're passionate about, you can be up-to-date on the latest information, and advertise yourself as the expert in those areas. It's also never too late to pick up a specialty and establish a niche for yourself. As a professional, you know you need to get the education and training for certain careers. If you pick a specialty you're passionate about, you'll enjoy learning about the latest research and going to niche conferences and events. It won't feel like work.

What if you're not sure what you want to specialize in? This can scare people away from private practice—and it shouldn't. I'd recommend taking clients in a few common areas in your field at first. As you get more time in business, you can see what you like and don't like. You can always take time to evaluate what's working (and not working!) in your practice, and make changes once you get some experience. As you expand your practice, you might realize that you want to make a change anyway. It's never too late!

Jill Lewis says...

Yes, you have to specialize! You should be drawn to your niche. As a therapist, you could specialize in so many areas, including trauma, eating disorders, substance abuse, children and play therapy, personality disorder, family therapy, just to name a few! This niche gives you grounding and access to making connections to a community that will support your career.

Your Ideal Client

No matter what type of counseling you practice, you have an ideal client. This client is the client that you can't wait to help solve their problems. You get energized and inspired by them! As an entrepreneur, you're constantly thinking about ways to help this client. Sound familiar?

I was recently introduced to a concept called the Ideal Client Scale by Dana Malstaff of Boss-Mom in the Raising Your Business program (affiliate link). I LOVE this scale and think about it often. At the bottom are the people who you want to help badly. They so need your help and guidance BUT they are either not ready for you OR can't pay you for your awesome work. **Why won't this work?** Trying to get these people the door is sadly a waste of time and energy. At the top are the people who have been transformed by your awesome work (whether it's from you or another similar program!) They love your work and believe in what you do. **Why won't this work?** These people don't have to pay you for your services, they have no problems to solve! In the middle are the people who believe in your message and need your help. They are ready for you and what you have to offer and are willing to pay for your services. **Why does this work?** It's the perfect match!

So much of the time we either market to the bottom or the top of the ideal client scale. We want to help everyone in our niche, and we also want to reach the people that really believe in our message and are "talking the talk and walking the walk". We really don't mean to do anything *wrong*, but zoning in even more on our ideal client (with problems to solve!) can help us much more in marketing and advertising services.

Your Vision Board for Success

A vision board helps business owners see a storyboard of what they want their business to look like. This can be a powerful tool for helping visualize success. A vision board is usually pictures, but can also be words on a sheet, which is used to try to come up with a business name or help you set your next business goals. In order to get started, write down words to represent your business, or take a few magazines and find pictures that speak to you. Try to remember your passion, and keep it positive. By visualizing what you want your business to look and feel like, you'll be able to visualize the big picture. This will eventually help you write out a business plan, which we'll talk about in the next chapter.

Step Three: Legally Form Your Business

As healthcare professionals, we've been trained in our field, and have adequate skills for our profession. However, most of us aren't trained in business! We may have had one or two courses in general business, but most of the time, healthcare professionals have no idea how to set up a business structure.

The Business Plan

Now that you know where you're going with your passion, you need to create a business plan. Some advisory sources might tell you to create a full report on your potential business, but you can also create an effective short version. You can make it from scratch or find a sample one online. Put your plan in writing, because seeing it on paper is more powerful than having ideas in your head. A business plan includes your mission, vision, simple goals and objectives, advisors, finances, and marketing and advertising information. Detailed information about this is included in the rest of the book. Now that you've figured out your passion, your business plan helps you set the stage for the road ahead.

The Business Mission

Your business mission is defined as the *purpose* of your company, and the focus of the work that you do. You can choose to keep your mission general or go as far as creating a name and tagline that's associated with your mission. Basically you want to get your message across in a clear and concise way.

Your business vision builds on your mission and takes you toward what you want your business to be in a certain number of years (typically 3-5 years). This may include increasing clients or doing consulting work, or perhaps selling a product.

By the way…

The mission of my private practice, Eat With Knowledge, is to help clients develop a healthy relationship with food, and to heal from disordered eating. My mission is my tagline, "Feel Fabulous about Food", which helps clients see exactly what I offer in just a few words. At first, my vision statement was to grow a part-time practice, 1-2 days per week, seeing 5-10 clients. As my business grew, my vision grew, as well. My mission statement changed to include running a full-time private practice and a consulting business.

Pick a Name for Your Business

Picking a business name is no easy task, but it's nevertheless a crucial step. You want your name to reflect your mission and vision by telling potential clients what you're all about. The hardest part about picking a name is choosing something that's original, because so many company names are already taken. It's also helpful to "google" potential names to see what results come back. Test your name with trusted colleagues, to see what they think. It's also helpful to test your name with random people, because they're less likely to hurt your feelings when it comes to the truth. Be sure to check to see if your business name is available on the internet by going to "yourbusinessname.com". If nothing is available with a .com ending, think about using .net, .biz, or .co in place of the .com. Unfortunately, ".com" is still considered the best extension for a company name.

By the way…

My first business name was "Bite Into Basics". I was so happy that I found something unique and not taken in the .com internet world. However when I started to test that name, many people told me I sounded like a dentist. I was so disappointed, because I was set on that name, but knew I should listen now before I got too attached. I eventually let it go, along with the .com purchase and started over.

What if you can't come up with a name? Use your own given name for legal purposes, and keep thinking about it. "[Your name] [Business area]" (dietitian Jane Smith would use "Jane Smith Nutrition") is always a backup option.

Decide on a Business Structure

Once you've picked a name, it's time to file and officially form your business. At this point, there are many options to legally file for a business, and there are pros and cons for each. As a **sole proprietor**, all you need to start your business is YOU! At the end of the year, you file a Schedule C as part of your personal IRS 1040 tax form, stating your income and expenses. This is the easiest way to form a business. However, it doesn't give you, personally, legal or financial separation from your business, and therefore, you're liable for all debts and legal obligations.

The next is a **Limited Liability Company (LLC)** or a **Professional Limited Liability Company (PLLC)**. To form one of these entities, you need to file with your state of residence, draft a business plan, and pay a filing fee. Some states require that you have a registered agent. Forming an LLC gives you legal and financial protection from debt, since now you and your business are considered separate. Because each state is different, it might be helpful to consult a lawyer or an accountant, or other healthcare professionals near you, to get specific advice. You can also use professional sites such as LegalZoom.

If you're going to be a **sole proprietor**, you need to file a "Doing Business As" (dba) paper with your local county clerk's office. This piece of paper states you have formed a company. You'll also need it to open a bank account in the name of the business, which will be discussed later. If you're forming an **LLC**, your paperwork will serve as proof of your business when you file.

> **Erica Leon, MS, RDN, CDN, CEDRD** is the owner of Erica Leon Nutrition. She is a Certified Eating Disorders Registered Dietitian and has an established private practice in White Plains, NY. Erica has written numerous articles for professional nutrition publications, is quoted in the media for her nutritional expertise, and serves as a frequent guest lecturer on eating disorder prevention and childhood weight issues.
>
> ### Erica Leon says...
>
> *For a period of time, I worked at home and saw clients in my home office. I wanted to keep personal and business life separate so I decided to open a PLLC (Professional Limited Liability Company). It's important for healthcare professionals to know that part of the purpose of the PLLC is to protect your personal finances.*

Get Insurance for Your Company

Once you've filed, it's time to protect yourself with professional liability business insurance, covering both you and your business. HPSO, and Proliability are two companies that have great plans for dietitians. Therapists can purchase a plan through the American Professional Agency. It's absolutely vital that you have business insurance to protect yourself if you're ever involved in a lawsuit.

Find Mentors to Help You

In the business world, you'll find many people who could be potential mentors, and it's helpful to have some of them on your team. First of all, surround yourself with other professionals who have done this before. Look for colleagues in your area, and make a connection. Find organizations that gather like-minded professionals, looking for connections in your field. People that have done this before know shortcuts and tips, and they can also have some amazing advice.

It's also helpful to identify an accountant and lawyer early on, in case they're needed, even if they're just on standby. An accountant can help you with taxes and can give advice regarding tax-deductible business expenses. Any legal fees, insurance, conferences, education, your car payment, office supplies, phone and printing costs are all probably tax-deductible. You may even expense this book cost as part of your education. Check with your accountant for any specific questions, as this can be a confusing subject for a lot of people. A lawyer can help you officially form an LLC, if needed, as well as help with policies and procedures of official business. A lawyer may also help write a contract or help with an employee agreement, as needed. It helps to have contacts ready, especially if there's some kind of business emergency.

By the way...

My best advice to new professionals is to network as much as possible, and find mentors to help you. It's very hard to know all the "right answers" in business, and that's why finding professionals to help mentor you is key to your success! Find professionals who are leaders in your field, and professionals that help you with business.

Step Four: Get Registrations and Finances in Order

There are certain registrations that are important when owning a company. Don't let the paperwork scare you, since these registrations can be completed quite quickly.

Employer Identification Number (EIN) or Tax-ID number

It's helpful to obtain an **Employer Identification Number (EIN)—a Tax-ID** number for your business. When you file information to the government, you use this to identify your business, much as your Social Security Number identifies YOU. You don't necessarily need this to open a business bank account, but if you have this number, it's smart to use it instead of your personal social security number. Also, if you plan on accepting insurance payments, companies will use this number as part of "registration" for insurance companies. Even if you don't plan on directly taking insurance, clients may want to use out-of-network benefits for reimbursement. If so, their insurance company will need your EIN number or your social security number: What would you rather give out? So apply for an EIN number or Tax-ED online <u>here</u>. It's a fairly easy process.

National Provider Identification (NPI) Number

It's a smart idea to apply for a **National Provider Identification (NPI)** number. This number identifies you as a healthcare professional, and helps with the transmission of healthcare information to insurance companies. This number is used for insurance reimbursement, regardless of whether you're taking insurance payments directly or having clients submit because you're an "out-of-network" provider.

If you're going to accept insurance in your practice, you need the NPI number in order to get on insurance panels and become an "in-network provider" with an insurance company. There are many pros and cons to taking insurance. In a nutshell, taking insurance allows you to grow faster and see more clients, but you may not get paid well (or even at all). By not taking insurance, you can charge what you're worth, but you may grow more slowly. It also depends on the population you're serving, and if they want to use their insurance for your sessions. Apply for a NPI number <u>here</u>.

Open a Bank Account

If you have a bank account with all of your business transactions, you'll have all of your financial information organized in one place. At the end of the calendar year, you'll be able to see your income and expenses, for tax purposes. By having everything in one account, you can easily see totals (or give the information to an accountant to file your taxes) and, therefore, you won't have to be adding up receipts by hand. It's also helpful to analyze this data to see trends in income or expenses or both. You can use an official software application like <u>Quickbooks</u> or <u>Freshbooks</u> to help you save time. This is helpful to see where you're spending money, broken down by category and percentage.

Set Up Your Practice to Take Payment

Taking electronic payment is a requirement in today's society. Credit cards are the most popular way to pay for services. There are many ways to set up your practice to take payment from clients. You can choose to accept payment before the session, during the session, or bill for payment after the session. A popular question among healthcare professionals is whether or not to take payment upfront before a session. Pros include getting your money as a deposit and practically guaranteeing that your client will show up. Cons include offending someone before meeting them and your client may not feel comfortable. It's up to you to decide what works best for your practice and organization.

Paypal, Venmo, and Square (affiliate link) are popular payment processing centers. Square is very easy to use if you have a smartphone, because you can connect your bank account to your Square account, and they send you a credit card reader for free. You can then use your credit card reader to accept payment with just your smartphone.

Keep in mind that, if you don't want to deal with credit cards, you can always tell clients that cash and check are preferred methods of payment. But you're making it harder for the client!

Step Five: Plan Your Schedule

One of the best tips in business is to use a calendar to get organized. If you're a naturally organized person, consider yourself lucky! Creating a calendar helps business owners know when they can book clients and stay on track with business tasks. Even if you're not the type to write everything down in a chronological order, you can start to set mini-goals for yourself and your business.

A calendar is essential when scheduling clients. It's helpful to have a block of hours available on the same day so you can schedule clients consistently. It's very easy to remember "My appointment is Mondays at 5:00" vs. changing the appointment time every week. There are many calendar systems available: a traditional "paper" calendar, google calendar, Cozi, or Acuity (affiliate link). The benefit of a synchronized technology calendar means that you can connect your calendar to your laptop, phone, ipad, etc. As you grow, you may even share your calendar with an administrative assistant.

No matter how many hours you have to set aside for business-related tasks, you should determine what you're doing with your time. This allows you to get the most productivity out of your investment in yourself. Flexibility is important, and your calendar may change, but what may seem like a lot of overhead is really a way of setting yourself up for success. If you're an organized person, this will be easy for you. If you aren't organized, try to set one overall goal for the day or week rather than focusing on the little details.

An electronic calendar may also connect to your electronic medical chart (or vice versa) as a way to schedule clients and appointments. We will talk more about this in an upcoming chapter. If you want consistency in appointments, you can also automatically schedule someone weekly or every other week so it shows up in future time. That way, you can see your future availability if you want to plan something in advance.

By the way…

When I started out, I had 1-2 days per week for private practice. Sometimes my schedule would work out that I had a few people back-to-back, but other times, I had one morning client and one evening client. It was helpful to have a to-do list for when this happened, guaranteeing that I never felt like I was wasting time. For me, I had to schedule my to-do's on my calendar, or else they'd never get done.

Remember, one of the "perks" of private practice is that YOU set your own schedule. Are you a morning person or an evening person? Do you want breaks in between clients, or would you rather see everyone back-to-back? Know what works with your personality, and you'll be successful with scheduling your business time.

Step Six: Find Counseling Space

Where are you going to do your work? Remember your vision and what you want your business to look like. Are you going to clients' homes and practicing there? Or are you having clients come to you? What does that space look like? Maybe it really matters to you what kind of space you work in, or maybe it doesn't. Having a calm and peaceful space is usually best for counseling, allowing clients to feel comfortable and open. Having neutral colors might also work best for serenity, as well as natural light to help with optimism and mood. Any counseling space should avoid intense color contrasts, and should not be too dark or uninviting.

It's also helpful to display some of your business "personality" in your office. Do you want your office to feel more "homey" with comfortable couches? Or do you want to sit behind a desk, with chairs in front, for a more formal approach? Also, think about décor on your walls and what you want it to represent. Some healthcare professionals have pictures of healthy foods, exercise, or calming mantras plastered on their walls. Does that suit your personality or not? Does the décor reflect your message and mission statement? Other professionals may prefer to keep their office somewhat blank, in order to be neutral and not project anything in sessions. It depends on your personality and style of counseling. Every business will be different, and it just depends on you.

Set Up Your Office

If you want to have clients come to your office, start to look around where you're located to see if there's a space you might be able rent. You could decide to lease your own space right away, or perhaps lease from another professional for one or two days per week. You just have to make sure that their space fits your personality. It's helpful to be in an area with other professionals. Just think of the networking possibilities! Consider looking at websites such as Craigslist and Loopnet to find office space to rent. You may also be able to rent an office by the hour in certain buildings, depending on your location. Go out to check buildings on your own. Sometimes, that's the best way to see if space is available. If you're just starting out, it's important to think about your budget and what you can afford. You can always move to a bigger space later.

Sometimes, it's helpful to rent a room in a larger space, such as a doctor's office, spa, or gym. It's instant advertising to have your service in a desired location, and it's helpful for you to network, by physically seeing potential professionals that may refer to you every day you're in the office. Think about your target market and who you're trying to make your services available to. Then think about a location where you'd find those potential clients, and see if space is available.

I rented a room, initially, that was mediocre, but it got the job done. I also rented the space to two other professionals, as a way to cut down my cost. Eventually, I moved into a nicer space, once I could afford it. But by spending more money on a space that fit my personality, I felt more confident and retained more clients, making me more money, even though I had to spend more to get there.

Christine Knorr, LCSW is the owner of her private practice. She is a Licensed Clinical Social Worker who has a private practice in Nyack, NY. She treats eating disorders, and specializes in children and adolescents, conduct disorders, and family therapy. She loves to help social workers realize their business potential and inspire clinicians to make a good living for themselves.

Christine Knorr says….

In the beginning of my private practice, I didn't know how long it would take to get clients, so I didn't have the money to rent an office. I decided to do home visits to first build up my practice. I was used to doing home visits in a previous job. Once I was ready for an office, I found one that rented by the hour. It doesn't have to be a therapist office; it could be a lawyer's office or another professional space. I just packed up my office with my supplies and traveled.

What Do You Need for Your Office?

The most important aspect of an office is YOU and your client working together on the counseling process. Honestly, that's your "office" and could be anywhere. However, keep in mind that you may eventually need office supplies in order to do a better job in private practice. Some helpful items may include: a computer, printer, phone, copier, the ability to fax documents, a credit card processing system, and business cards. You may also choose to keep a safe (or locked box) that contains charts, as well as a file cabinet for handouts to give to clients. Depending on your profession, you may also need equipment. A dietitian may need measuring cups to estimate portions, and a fitness professional may need exercise equipment. Your counseling space may or may not include all of these things, depending on whether you have a home office or a rented professional space. Remember, these are all tax-deductible expenses.

Most importantly if you're just starting out, all you really need is YOU! You are the one providing the service, so you can buy the rest of what you need as you go. Remember that you don't need to spend a huge amount of money at the beginning; you can invest as you go along.

Jill Weisenberger, MS, RDN, CDE, FAND is the owner of her private practice <u>Food and Nutrition Solutions by Jill</u>. She is a Registered Dietitian, Certified Diabetes Educator, and freelance writer. Her philosophy is that nutrition science should be understandable, realistic and "oh so delicious"—nothing boring, super-restrictive, overwhelming or scientifically unsound. Her goal now, and for the last two decades, has been to empower people to grab control of their health. As a speaker and writer, she engages and entertains her audience while informing. She's the author of three books, and regularly contributes to a number of publications, including *Environmental Nutrition, Food & Nutrition Magazine, Diabetic Living, Kid's Eat Right, The DX,* and *Today's Dietitian.*

Jill Weinsenberger says...

Do not be afraid to spend money on your business! Get good tools that work for you and that will give back to your business. Consider hiring individuals to help you, because it's an investment in your business. Time-saving technology, a professional looking logo and website, and help with consulting projects, like a book proposal, are all worth it!

Step Seven: Create Your Forms

Health professionals need forms for client visits, referrals, as well as a receipt for payment, usually either a bill for the session or a superbill. A professional should tailor forms for his or her client population, to make the gathering of information easy. Creating forms on your own is a great idea, since it allows you to personalize them to the type of client you are seeing. However, you can save time (and energy!) by purchasing or downloading a package of forms for a private practice; these are offered by many companies.

Assessment Forms

An assessment form for the initial session may include questions about demographics, as well as pertinent information that will depend on your profession. An initial assessment form may include as little or as much of this information as you need:

- Name, birthday, phone number, address
- Medical history (mental health and physical health), hospitalizations, current medications
- Height, weight, growth history and trends
- Family history (mental health and physical health)
- Nutrition information: Meals and snacks, 24 hour recall
- Exercise information: Frequency, type, and time spent
- Personalized information related to your practice

A follow-up form may ask about any changes since the last visit, as well as goals made at the last session. Again, it will depend on your profession and niche in private practice.

By the way…

Many professionals have their initial assessment forms online, so clients can download them before the first appointment. When I was first starting out, I viewed other dietitian's assessment forms to see what they were asking. I then created my own form, using theirs as a guide. Mine is available to download (for free) from www.eatwithknowledge.com.

Policies and Procedures

In private practice, it's important to set up policies and procedures according to your type of practice, your ethics, and your reputation. Your policies and procedures may change as you grow and evolve. Here are some examples of policies and procedures and the appropriate forms you may need.

- Office Policy Information (information on insurance, cancellations, and privacy)

- Credit Card Authorization form (if applicable)
- Authorization to Release Information (to other professionals)
- HIPAA (Health Insurance Portability and Accountability Act). This act sets standards for communication among healthcare providers if you exchange information with insurance companies. It's a good idea to follow this guideline, even if you don't accept insurance directly in your practice.
- Referral Summary to Referring Professionals and Fax Cover Sheet
- Sample Contract for any consulting work
- Receipt for visits or superbill for your client to use out-of-network benefits for an insurance company. A superbill should contain your NPI number, Tax ID number, diagnostic code(s) and procedure code, as well as your practice information.

There are many options available for dietitians to purchase forms. RD411 provides free assessment forms that are general, so you can make them your own. You can also purchase forms from Making Nutrition Your Business by Faye Berger Mitchell, RD, LDN and Ann Silver, MS, RD, CDE, CDN. Faye teamed up with Yvette Quantz of Customized Nutrition Newsletters to personalize nutrition assessment forms. You can purchase their forms here.

Basic Handouts

Now that you've figured out what your practice niche is, you know what kind of clients you'll be seeing. Therefore, you can develop (or purchase) handouts pertaining to your business. Dietitians may want handouts on meal planning, snack ideas, eating disorders, or sports nutrition. Therapists may wish to have handouts on mood changes, challenging harmful thoughts, and behavior change. It's also a good idea to have handouts on different diseases.

Any healthcare professional can make a handout by printing accurate, reliable information from the internet. However, it's not necessary to have lots of handouts before you start your private practice. Most of the time, clients want personalized advice, so a tailored note of suggestions just for them is much more desirable than general information.

By the way...

I created many handouts before officially starting my practice. For some reason, this made me feel "safe"—that I'd be able to educate clients, no matter what came up in sessions. Fast forward a few years, and my confidence has grown to the point that I don't need handouts anymore! However, I still keep a few for clients to take home as references or for more information. The best "handout" is a personalized note describing a few goals or ideas that you talked about during the session. I keep a notepad of paper, with my contact information written at the top, and write out goals for clients almost every session.

Step Eight: Set Up a Charting System

A medical chart is a record of client visits that's important for documentation of client sessions. Each session should be documented with an accompanying note. Some insurance companies may also audit client medical records. It's also proper documentation of visits if you're ever involved in a lawsuit.

There are many medical charting systems to choose from, ranging from free to expensive, and simple to complicated. As a business owner, you have to decide what system works with your practice. The old-fashioned charting system is done on paper for each client, which includes follow-up notes after each visit, and are locked up for safe keeping. However, electronic charting is the wave of the future. Examples useful to all healthcare professionals include Practice Fusion, and Practice Mate (which is also coupled with Office Ally for billing purposes). MNT Assistant, Kalix, and Healthie are other medical record for dietitians. For therapists, Theranest and Therapynotes are popular medical records. Practice Better and Simple Practice (affiliate link) are medical record that works for many counseling professionals.

What should you include in a chart note? There are many options, but it ultimately depends on what you feel is important and what's required by your profession. Medical notes may include medical history, height & weight, growth history, medications, and current diagnosis. Therapy notes may be more subjective, and may include an assessment on thoughts, behaviors, and challenges. The most important part of any note is the underlining summary of the visit and anything planned for the next visit. It's very helpful to have this to refer to when seeing clients, so you can keep everyone straight!

By the way...

As a dietitian, I was trained to write clinical ADIME notes (sections for Assessment, Diagnosis, Intervention, Monitoring, and Evaluation). However, I always felt that a simple SOAP note worked best for me (Subjective, Objective, Assessment and Plan). There's no right or wrong way to write a note. The only requirement is that your client's health information be private and protected.

Step Nine: Set Up Your Services

A client comes to see you because you offer something they need. Whatever profession you're in, a client is paying you because you're offering them a solution to a problem. There are many "problems" to be fixed, and therefore, many creative ways to offer solutions and make money doing so.

What Are Services You Can Offer?

Depending on your target client population, you may choose to set up different services for your target market. Most of the time, healthcare professionals in private practice choose to offer counseling services for clients. This may be in the form of individual counseling services, family counseling, or group counseling. This type of service may include a set fee for a specific amount of time. Typically, payment would be taken at the session, but it may also be billed as a package or charged monthly.

Counselors may also choose to engage in virtual counseling sessions, using Skype or the telephone. Check with your individual state on licensing regulations, but know that this is an area that's growing very fast.

If a client is engaged in regular sessions, a professional may choose to offer an add-on service, if needed. This could be a group session, an additional family session, or a non-traditional session that takes place outside of the typical counseling setting. This is a great way to offer more care, while increasing client satisfaction and increasing revenue.

Jill Lewis says…

I see individual clients for therapy, but I also run a group. A group setting provides a place for clients to explore past and present dynamics, enactments, and tackle issues with those who have faced similar challenges and can relate to the struggle. Many clients choose to add this on to their therapy with me.

Create Packages

It may be beneficial to create packages for your clients. This is something that's very helpful for many healthcare professionals, because clients see an entire package in front of them and know exactly what they are getting. They could also see a "deal" in front of them by reducing the price if you buy a package upfront. You would charge appropriately, depending on your time involved. When clients commit to a package, you don't have to worry about getting paid every week or if they might drop out of your program. Every package should have guidelines and policies in place, and should be signed by the client. You may also wish to set up a way to organize this in your client calendar. You now have your client's commitment. You have to be just as committed.

Erica Leon says...

I offer Healthy Habits, which is family based program for helping children develop a positive relationship with eating and a neutral relationship with food, using an "everyday" vs. "sometimes food" philosophy. The goal is to teach families and children how to honor hunger and fullness, embrace exercise, and manage emotional eating. When parents pay up front for the program they are more engaged, and committed to following through.

There may be hesitation from clients about committing to a lot of sessions, or even paying a higher amount for all these sessions. Just a reminder that charging clients per week is very normal, and charging for add-ons as you go is also fine. Every practice is different!

Step Ten: Figure Out How Much to Charge

One of the biggest decisions in business is how much to charge for your services. It's very hard to pinpoint exactly how much to charge, but you can always start lower and increase when you want to. You can also find out what other professionals around you are charging per session. A basic tip on how much to charge—when you have more clients than you can handle, it means it's time to increase your fee.

What's Your Target Income?

Depending on your life and desires, you're going to come up with a target income that's right for you. Of course we all want to make a million dollars! But more realistically, think about your target income as an overall reflection of your expertise, your competition, and your choice of clients. Once you know how much you want to make as a target income, you can figure out how much to charge per hour. This will depend on your expenses, which may include rent, car payment, health insurance, taxes, and office expenses like paper, ink, and other supplies. Additional expenses may include credentialing, continuing education conferences, and advertising/promotions. Once you know your target income and expenses, you'll know how much you need to earn to reach your goal.

When you're just starting out, you have no established track record in private practice to prove your worth. Start here as a guide and remember you can always increase. Once you get into a business groove, you'll have more control over how much you want to work and the price that you can or want to charge. Remember that there are a lot of variables when it comes to business expenses, such as how much you want to work, and what your time is worth.

So What Should You Charge Per Hour?

Let's look at two different scenarios for your potential private practice. Each scenario has its own target income for learning purposes.

The first scenario is that you have a steady job, but want to open up a practice on the side. You're going to rent office space one day per week, and expenses are low. You only want to work 2 days per week for 5 hours each day, or a total of 10 hours per week. Suppose you want to earn $15,000-$20,000 per year from your practice for it to be worthwhile being in business. Keep in mind that, if you have a range, aim high, because you'll have to pay income and/or business taxes. Assume that your expenses will be about $1,000 per month.

In addition, you may want to take a vacation, and you may want to allow for some sick time. So, let's say you work 45 weeks out of the year. 45 weeks x 10 hours per week = 450 hours. Keep in mind that sometimes you won't get paid for all of these hours because part of this time will include marketing, billing, networking, etc. You will want to take this into consideration once you have your average hourly rate (HR).

Scenario #1:

Goal income = Total revenue charged – Expenses

$20,000 = (450 hours x "HR" [Your Hourly Rate]) – ($1,000 x 12 months)

$20,000 = 450 "HR" - $12,000

Now solve for "HR"

450 "HR" = $20,000 + $12,000

"HR" = $71.11 per hour. Basically, on average, you want to bring in about $700/week for those 45 weeks worked per year. If you need $700/week, how many clients does that mean you will need to see and how much will you charge them?

The second scenario is that you want to make $100,000 per year, working with clients 30 hours per week but working on your business full-time. Of course, you know that there will be at least 10 hours per week that is used on your business, just not client time. In order to get those 10 hours covered by your clients, your calculations have to be done based on 30 hours of work time. Let's just suppose that your expenses average about $3,000 per month. Again, assume you work 45 weeks out of the year (45 weeks x 30 hours per week = 1,350 hours).

Scenario #2:

Goal Income = Total revenue charged – Expenses

$100,000 = (1,350 hours x "HR" [Your Hourly Rate]) – ($3,000 x 12 months)

$100,000 = 1,350 "HR" - $36,000

Now solve for "HR"

1,350 "HR = $100,000 + $36,000

"HR" = $100.74 per hour. Basically, on average, you will have to bring in about $3,000/week for those 45 weeks worked per year. If you need $3,000/week, how many clients does that mean you will need to see and how much will you charge them?

Ask around to see what other professionals charge per hour. There's usually a full range of prices, ranging from inexpensive to overpriced. There's a benefit to starting on the lower end of the scale—it usually gives you more confidence in offering your services, especially knowing that clients are probably shopping around. You may also feel that you want to grow your business fast. Charging on the lower end of the range allows you to grow faster, because more clients will take advantage of your services. On the flipside, there's a benefit to starting on the higher end of the range. People believe that a higher price represents quality work. With this belief, some clients may actually *want* to pay higher fees, especially for someone who specializes in their particular need. Starting on the higher end of the range may also be beneficial, since it gives you some room to adjust your fee if you're experiencing a slower time. During those weeks or months, you could offer a discount, which has its pros and cons. But it can be worthwhile when used appropriately.

Jill Lewis says...

There are usually standard rates for new clinicians, a higher rate for someone who has experience, and the highest rate for an expert. Where do you rank? Remember your bottom line per hour and your value and worth. If a client needs to pay under that rate, you may choose to refer that client out, unless you really want to increase your clients!

What is Your Time Worth?

An important factor to consider is the value of your time. You may have perfect equations to figure out the perfect target income, but when it comes down to it, you may have a better "gut feeling" about what to charge based on the value of your time. Remember, there's no right answer as to "what to charge". It's quite subjective. Do what's right for you! This is one of many examples to show you that every business owner will need to make individualized decisions that work for their own private practice.

Pursuing Private Practice Programs

Congratulations on completing this book! I'm so excited that you've gotten a head start on how to pick a niche that's meaningful and special to you. You've learned how to take that passion and set up a practice that makes you the expert in your field. You have built the base of an incredible private practice and you are on your way to becoming your own boss. Please make sure you continue to read the next book in the Pursuing Private Practice book series: *Pursuing Private Practice, 10 Steps to Grow Your Own Business.*

If you found this book helpful, you will love other resources from Pursuing Private Practice.

I want to empower dietitians to build their confidence in nutrition counseling AND growing their business. To be able to run a business seeing as many clients as they want, doing the important work of intuitive eating and eating disorder recovery.

Make the Dream of Being Your Own Boss a Reality

Build the Private Practice of Your Dreams

Introducing…. Pursuing Private Practice® for Intuitive Eating!

This program is the ONLY program that teaches dietitians and nutritionists how to successfully grow a private practice that specializes in Intuitive Eating.

Are you feeling stuck? Overwhelmed? Scared? But also excited about starting and growing a business? Being an entrepreneur is not easy and all of these feelings are normal. You may feel lost in business training and not sure about how to counsel clients in intuitive eating and eating disorder recovery.

Trust me... I get it. I built my business from absolutely nothing when I moved to the suburbs of NYC in 2010. I wasted so much time "trying to figure it out" and "get everything perfect" before I officially opened. I also needed more training in intuitive eating and how to run a weight-inclusive business. I only WISH I had this course back then because it would have given me the confidence and solutions needed for success in business and seeing clients.

Gift yourself this program. It's not only a gift for YOU to make your life easier, but a gift to your business. This course will help you run your business more efficiently and teach you tips and tricks for success. And "success" can mean whatever you want it to mean, including working part-time! Do the important work on intuitive eating that you were meant to do as a dietitian or healthcare profession. Join the program to be the dietitian you were meant to be.

Here are the details....

- Business Foundations: 10 modules on starting and growing a private practice
- *For Professionals: Help Your Clients Feel Fabulous About Food* course
- A workbook full of personalized exercises you can do for your business
- Facebook® group for accountability, discussions, and Q and A
- Forms, templates and handouts you can use with your clients
- Group coaching calls once/month to ask me anything
- Various trainings on business and nutrition

For Registered Dietitians: this course has been approved for 13 CEU credits given by the Commission on Dietetic Registration.

A special thank you:

Get on my email list to receive more information about the course plus lots of tips on business and private practice. When you sign up, you receive a free mini training on private practice as well! Sign up at www.pursuingprivatepractice.com.

If you have any questions about the program, please email Jennifer McGurk at jennifer@eatwithknowledge.com. We will set up an inquiry call to talk about your business and to find out if the program is the right fit for you.

Useful Resources

These resources were used when writing the *Pursuing Private Practice* book series:

Francis, Ronald. *Private Practice Psychology: A Handbook. BPS Books, 2001.*

Geiser, Marjorie. *Just Jump: The No- Fear Business Start-up Guide for Health and Fitness Professionals. California Based Publishing, Running Springs CA, 2008.*

Greenberg, Kait Fortunato, Rebecca Blitzer, and Dana Magee. *Welcome to Rebelution: 7 Steps to the Nutrition Counseling of Your Dreams. Empowered Enterprises, 2014.*

King, Kathy, RD. LD. *The Entrepreneurial Nutritionist. LWW, 2009.*

Lanci, Mark, and Anne Spreng. *The Therapist's Starter Guide: Setting Up and Building Your Practice, Working with Clients, and Managing Professional Growth. John Wiley and Sons, Hobokon, NJ, 2008.*

Mitchell Faye Berger, and Ann Silver. *Making Nutrition Your Business. Academy of Nutrition and Dietetics, 2010.*

National Association of Social Workers www.socialworkers.org, Practice and Professional Development, Specialty Groups, Private Practice.

Nutrition Entrepreneurs Practice Group and listserv: www.nedpg.org.

Zuckeran, Edward, PhD. *The Paper Office, Third Edition: Forms Guidelines and Resources to make Your Practice work Ethically, Legally, and Profitably. Guilford Press, New York, NY, 2008.*

Helpful Resources for Business and Private Practice:

Buy and sell digital products: RD2RD

Dietitian HQ and bi-annual RD Symposium: www.dietitianhq.com

Alissa Rumsey NYC mastermind retreat: http://alissarumsey.com/mastermindretreat

Dietitian Institute: http://dietitianinstitute.com

Facebook groups:

- #INSPIRDTOSEEK
- Fearless Practitioners
- RD Entrepreneurs
- Mindset and Marketing Mastery for Dietitians in Virtual Practice
- Elevate Your Business
- Selling the Couch

Podcasts:

- My own show, the Pursuing Private Practice podcast!
- Selling the Couch
- Practice of the Practice
- Being Boss
- Boss Mom
- Online Marketing Made Easy
- Smart Passive Income
- Biz Chix Women Entrepreneurs
- Productivity Paradox
- Legal Road Map
- RD Real Talk (there are many episodes about private practice)

Productivity Resources

Task management: Trello

Project management and team communication: Basecamp

Save passwords: Dashlane

Store documents: Dropbox (affiliate link)

Sanebox email management (affiliate link)

About The Author

Jennifer McGurk, RDN, CDN, CEDRD-S is a Registered Dietitian Nutritionist whose mission is to help people heal from diets, and find peace and balance with their food choices. She is the owner of Eat With Knowledge in Nyack, NY. She leads a team of dietitians who support the philosophy, "*Feel fabulous about food*!" and created an online course of the same name for clients. She also created "*For Professionals: Help Your Clients Feel Fabulous About Food*" to train healthcare professionals on nutrition counseling for intuitive eating and eating disorder recovery.

As a Certified Eating Disorders Registered Dietitian, Jennifer combines her expertise in medical nutrition therapy, psychology, and physiology to help clients understand their eating behaviors, and gain the insight needed to make positive changes for their health. She is an expert in the field of eating disorders and also supervises other Registered Dietitians. She is involved with the International Federation of Eating Disorder Dietitians, the National Eating Disorders Association, and the International Association of Eating Disorder Professionals (iaedp).

Having completed her undergraduate training at Pennsylvania State University in Nutritional Sciences, she continued to Johns Hopkins Bayview Medical Center in Baltimore, MD, to complete her dietetic internship. She received her Certified Diabetes Educator credential in 2009 and her Certified Eating Disorders Registered Dietitian credential in 2014. Jennifer has professional affiliations with the Academy of Nutrition and Dietetics and Nutrition Entrepreneurs.

Jennifer has created the business, Pursuing Private Practice, to help other healthcare professionals reach their goal of owning their own business. *Pursuing Private Practice: 10 Steps to Start Your Own Business* was her first book released in January 2016, and *Pursuing Private Practice: 10 Steps to Grow Your Own Business* was released in April 2016. The Pursuing Private Practice Course was released in April 2017. The *Pursuing Private Practice for Intuitive Eating* program was released March 2019.

Jennifer is a frequent guest in the media, often talking about positive nutrition, body image, healing from dieting, and educating others about eating disorders. She also loves to talk about all topics related to private practice! She has given presentations at conferences and workshops to audiences from 10 to as many as 1,000 people, and has been featured in news articles and on podcasts. For Jennifer, each presentation is an opportunity to share with her audience her positive message about food.

Find her at www.pursuingprivatepractice.com and www.eatwithknowledge.com.

Acknowledgements

It truly takes a village and a supportive community to accomplish any dream. This book is no exception! So many mentors have contributed to all of my professional career dreams and I am so thankful for the support. I would not be the professional I am today without my personal life experience, so I also need to acknowledge my support system.

Thank you to my family for all of your encouragement. To my husband Pat, thank you for giving me the support I needed to write this book. To my sons Connor and Aidan, both of you inspire me to be the best person I can be -- always follow your dreams and know that you can do anything you want to do. Thank you to my parents and my extended family, as well.

To my clients -- I could never have built such a successful private practice without all of you. It's an honor to work with you on a journey to a positive relationship with food. The changes I've seen in all of you have truly impacted me professionally and personally.

Thank you to my individual supervisors and peer supervisors, Jessica Setnick, Sumner Brooks, Rebecca Scritchfield, Julie Dillon, Lindsay Stenovec, Marci Evans, Rebecca Bitzer, and my Westchester Rockland eating disorder dietitian crew. You've all taught me so much about counseling and business, and I'm so thankful for your advice. We lift each other up!

Thank you to all of my colleagues who contributed their thoughts and expertise to this book series -- Christine Knorr, Arden Greenspan-Goldberg, Jill Lewis, Faye Berger Mitchell, Jill Weisenberger, and Erica Leon. Thank you for your guidance!

Thank you to all of my teachers and role models along the way. I am forever grateful for the Penn State nutrition department, the Women's Leadership Initiative, and the teachers at Johns Hopkins Bayview Medical Center. I have met so many inspiring dietitians in my career, it would be impossible to list them all!

To Kristin Quill, Stephanie Gebhart, Roberta and Larry Wennik -- thank you for all the hard work on the book with research, design, writing coaching, and editing.

Finally, to International Federation of Eating Disorder Dietitians (IFEDD) and Nutrition Entrepreneurs (NE)-- my favorite dietitian communities. I am forever grateful for all you have taught me! Cheers to successful entrepreneurs and thriving private practices!

Made in the USA
San Bernardino, CA
16 July 2020